DINKY DEER IS LOST

BY JUNE WOODMAN
ILLUSTRATED BY PAMELA STOREY

Brimax Books · Newmarket · England

Dinky Deer is in the forest.
She is looking for her mother.
"I am lost," she says.
"I cannot find my mother."
Dinky Deer is all alone in
the dark forest. She is not
very happy.
"I must find my mother,"
she says. Dinky sets off
to look for her.

Dinky jumps out onto the forest path. Cuddly Cat is on the path.

"OH!" says Cuddly.

She drops her basket, and all her cakes fall out.

"I am lost," says Dinky.

"Have one of my cakes," says Cuddly. "Then we will go and find your mother."

They pick up the rest of the cakes, then they go off together. Soon they come to the duck pond. Dilly Duck is there. She is very cross.

"Look at my three silly little ducklings," she says. The ducklings are by the pond. It is very muddy. The ducklings are muddy too. Dilly washes them clean.

"I am lost," says Dinky to the three ducklings.
"We will help you," they all say.
"I will help too," says Dilly.
So Dinky Deer, Cuddly Cat, Dilly and her ducklings all set off to look for Mother Deer.
Soon they come to Bossy Bear's house. He is washing his windows.

The three little ducklings
run up to Bossy. They make
him jump and he drops his
bucket. The water falls out
all over Dilly Duck.
"OH!" says Dilly. "You are
silly little ducklings!" She is
all wet and VERY cross.
"I am lost," says Dinky.
"I will help you," says Bossy.

So they all set off to look for Mother Deer. Dinky and Cuddly Cat, Dilly and her ducklings and Bossy Bear all go down the lane together. Soon they come to Paddy Dog's house. He is busy painting his gate.
The three little ducklings run up to him.

"Dinky Deer is lost!" they call out. It makes Paddy jump. He drops the paint, and it goes all over them.

"OH!" say the ducklings. Dilly Duck is VERY cross.

"I cannot find my mother," says Dinky. "I am lost." She is very sad.

"I will help you," says Paddy Dog.

So Dinky Deer, Cuddly Cat,
Dilly and her ducklings,
Bossy Bear and Paddy Dog
all set off together.
Soon they come to Hoppy
Rabbit's house. He is
very busy washing his
little car.
The ducklings run to him.
They make him jump and he
falls over his bucket. Now
he is wet and cross.
But Dinky Deer is sad.

Dinky tells Hoppy Rabbit
that she is lost.
"I will help you," says Hoppy.
So Dinky Deer, Cuddly Cat,
Dilly and her ducklings,
Bossy Bear, Paddy Dog and
Hoppy Rabbit all go off together
"Look up there!" says Paddy.
They look up into a tree.
They see Ozzie Owl. He is
asleep. The three little
ducklings run to the tree.

"Dinky Deer is lost!" they call. They make him jump. Ozzie Owl falls out of the tree. "OW!" he says. He is very cross. "Have you seen Mother Deer?" says Cuddly Cat.
"She is in the forest," says Ozzie. "Come with me."
So Dinky, Cuddly, Dilly, the ducklings, Bossy, Paddy, Hoppy and Ozzie go to the forest together.

Merry Mole and Flippy Frog
are in the forest. They are
busy picking blackberries.
The ducklings run up to them.
"Dinky Deer is lost!" they
call. Merry and Flippy
fall into the bush.
"OW!" they say.
The blackberries all fall
out of their basket.
"You three are silly!"
say Merry and Flippy.

Dinky Deer begins to cry.
"I am lost," she says.
"I cannot find my mother!"
"LOOK!" say Merry and Flippy.
Someone is coming round the
blackberry bush.
It is Mother Deer.
"Here I am, Dinky," she says.
"You are not lost now. Do not
cry, little Dinky."

Now Dinky is very happy.
Mother Deer is happy, too.
Merry and Flippy pick up
all the blackberries and
the ducklings help them.
Then they all sit down
under the trees together.
They eat the cakes
and blackberries.
"Thank you," says Dinky to
all her friends, "I am not
lost now!"

Say these words again

lost	muddy
alone	helps
own	bucket
jumps	blackberries
drops	asleep
basket	happy
together	here